TAKE CHARGE
OF YOUR DIET
A SELF-HELP
WORKBOOK USING
COGNITIVE
BEHAVIOURAL
THERAPY

First published by Ortus Press,
an imprint of Free Association Books
Copyright © 2021 Sylvie Boulay
The authors rights are fully asserted. The rights of
Sylvie Boulay to be identified as the author of this work
has been asserted by her in accordance with the
Copyright, Designs and Patents Act 1988

A CIP Catalogue of this book is available from the British Library

ISBN: 978-1-911-38360-4

Typeset by Typo•glyphix
www.typoglyphix.co.uk

Cover design by Candescent
Illustrations by Sylvie Boulay

Printed and bound in England

CONTENTS

To Dee and Lyra who fill my life with joy

A MESSAGE TO YOU

This workbook is the result of a lifelong journey I started in secondary school and I am now the grandmother of a teenager. As I grew up, I used food as a coping mechanism and carried this on into adulthood. All my life, I gained weight then dieted and never stayed at the same weight for more than a few months. I don't want to think how much weight I put on, lost and put back on over the years. Then I made a late career change, retrained and started to work as a therapist with clients who were addicted to drugs, alcohol and gambling.

At first, I found it difficult to relate to them because I have no personal experience of these addictions. I thought I might be able to understand their struggles if I used my own battle with weight. Soon it struck me that the techniques I was using in my client work could directly be applied to my own overeating. I eventually found a healthy way of eating to keep excess weight off for good and this is what I want to share with you in this workbook. The lightbulb moment was realising that success had nothing to do with finding the perfect diet, or the perfect life for that matter. I needed to work on what was going on in my brain around food. Once I became fully aware of my eating, I could make a conscious choice about what to eat and I stopped overeating most of the time.

Ten years ago, I was obsessed with my weight and my size. Now I think of myself as a healthy eater, a parkrunner and a cyclist. It's not that those things are the most important in my life but they are an essential part of how I choose to define myself. My relationship with food isn't perfect but it is good enough and my weight is stable within a reasonable range. This is the place I wish for you, where you are not preoccupied with your weight and are able to enjoy eating as a wonderful way of nourishing your body.

My aim is for you to start to eat consciously. This is not something I could have managed in a vacuum. I needed some sort of framework to follow – the tools and the techniques I learned with my clients. They worked for me and I hope they do for you.

In this workbook, I have adapted the techniques used for problem drinkers and drug users to people who find it difficult to lose weight. Most of my recommendations come from the field of Cognitive Behavioural Therapy (CBT) which was originally developed to treat depression but is one of the recognised treatments for addiction problems (See Branch and Willson if you want to learn more about CBT).

In the next chapters I will take you through ten stages to help you achieve and keep your ideal weight. I will show you how to observe your behaviour around food and make sense of your experience in a scientific but also a caring way. Once you understand what is going on, you can intervene and take action to avoid the behaviours which lead to weight gain.

The ten stages are easy to understand but there is nothing easy about doing them. Self-knowledge comes at a price: you need to work at it but it will be infinitely more productive than all the time and energy you have spent until now worrying about weight and diets. Do remember you will not have to work hard forever. Once you have figured out what works for you, food can be a pleasure rather than an enemy.

We will work through several exercises together. Some of them will appeal to you and others may not feel relevant right now. I will go through each one in turn so you can pick and choose what is right for you. The idea is for you to become your own weight loss therapist because no one knows you like you do and only you can decide what works best.

This workbook focuses on you: what goes on when you are tempted to eat too much, what has happened to your dieting efforts in the past and how you can make changes so you are successful next time. We are building your toolbox together and by the time you get to the end you will have developed new habits to slip into (almost) effortlessly and you will be in control of your eating and your weight most of the time. This workbook is not ultimately about successful dieting; it is about treating yourself with kindness and living a freer life.

1

IS THIS WORKBOOK FOR YOU?

Obesity has become a major issue in Western societies and there is a risk that some children will live shorter lives than their parents because of it. The UK Tackling Obesity Strategy found that around two thirds of adults are above a healthy weight and, of these, half are living with obesity (Department of Health and Social Care 2020). We know that excess weight can lead to major health problems and this has been highlighted by the COVID-19 pandemic. There has been an increased emphasis on surgical solutions to weight loss and every week brings more new diets which prescribe what foods should be eaten or avoided.

Most people trying to lose weight focus on 'how' they can lose weight; that is, on the actual diet. They concentrate on the food itself and ignore the fact that they are responsible for what they put in their mouths. A calorie is just a calorie, whether it comes from lettuce or chips, and dieters will only lose weight if they consume less calories than they burn. Any diet will work if a person follows it for long enough. After a while hunger, rebellion or sheer boredom set in and they end up back at square one, or worse, having put on a few more kilos. Then the vicious cycle of dieting and overeating swings in motion.

IS THIS WORKBOOK FOR YOU?

- Do you worry about your weight and your eating?
- Do you regularly feel out of control around food?
- Do you sometimes eat very quickly before you realise what you are doing?
- Have you tried every new diet, lost weight and then put it all back on?
- Do certain foods 'call to you' irresistibly even when you are not hungry?
- Do you crave sugary or fatty foods when you are upset, sad, angry, tired or bored?
- Do you lack confidence that you can lose weight and keep it off?

If you answered yes to most of these questions and are ready to take responsibility for your eating, then this workbook is for you. It applies whether you are happy with your weight but worry about keeping it off or whether you have a little or a lot to lose. It applies whether your issue is eating larger portions than you need, overeating certain foods or eating too many snacks. There are no good or bad foods. A healthy meal of lean protein, vegetables and fruit can still contain too many calories if portions are too big for your needs. Please note that this workbook is intended for adults only.

The idea of this workbook is very simple: the key to losing weight successfully isn't about what you eat but about what goes on in your brain. You can learn to become attuned to your thoughts and your feelings so that your eating behaviour becomes conscious. Once you understand what is happening in your head and your body, you are in charge of your eating.

I want you to reach a point where you eat because food is vital nourishment for your body and a great pleasure, not a way of smoothing negative emotions or passing the time. If you understand yourself in relation to food, you can control what you eat. By control, I don't mean following some rigid plan; I mean exercising conscious choice. If, like me, you have been a chronic dieter, having that choice will set you free to stop worrying about weight issues and get on with what really matters to you.

A word of caution: we are all on a spectrum, from totally healthy eating to serious eating problem. This workbook is aimed at people in the middle who have an issue with their weight but do not suffer from an eating disorder. If you have any concerns about your eating patterns or your body image or you think you may have an eating disorder like anorexia, bulimia or binge eating disorder or a combination of these, please speak to your doctor. Eating disorders are serious mental health issues but help is available and treatment can be very effective. If you are not sure, go to your GP anyway and also check out the resources and references in the appendix. Some of the techniques and tools discussed in this workbook could still be helpful but dieting itself is definitely not appropriate for people with eating disorders.

There is an on-going debate about the cultural pressure to conform to unattainable body images. This workbook does not suggest that any particular size or shape is desirable. It is intended to help readers who have decided to lose weight but who are finding it very difficult.

For most people wanting to lose weight, the solution lies in changing their relationship to food so that they eat a bit less and move a bit more to attain that calorie deficit. I shall use the word 'diet' as a shorthand for whatever programme is chosen to achieve this. It could be following a healthy eating plan, an exercise regime or a specific weight loss diet.

Rather than proposing yet another special diet, to be abandoned after a while, I will take you through ten stages which will help you to change your attitude to eating so you keep to whatever weight loss plan you choose. The answer lies in retraining your brain as well as your stomach. You can lose weight and maintain your weight loss if you monitor what you are thinking and doing instead of reaching for food on automatic pilot. This workbook offers ten stages to follow and the practical tools to use on your journey. It will help you learn from your experience and develop the skills to be your own weight loss coach.

I offer tips and suggestions but I don't recommend one specific way of losing weight. I deliberately don't offer advice on nutrition or exercise because good advice can easily be found elsewhere (see online Live Well – NHS Choices or The British Dietetic Association website. Also check out the weight loss actions in the PREVAIL Trial (Nuffield Dept of

Primary Care Health Sciences 2020)). Any programme based on sound nutrition and increased activity will work providing you consume less food than your body uses. It is for you to choose what works best for you. Take from this workbook what you need and stay open minded.

2

THE TEN STAGES
IN A NUTSHELL

We would have no weight problems if we could eat only when we are hungry and stop as soon as we are full. This is natural for small children who are offered a good range of food and allowed to make their own choices. As adults with a weight problem, we can't go back to our childhood, but we can re-train ourselves to develop a healthier relationship with food.

It would be great if we could just eat to satisfy hunger, but unfortunately we also eat to meet a wide variety of emotional needs, for instance, to get temporary relief from feelings of anger, anxiety or boredom. There may be times when we eat on automatic pilot: reaching for food becomes a reflex reaction in response to a situation and it can feel as if food is calling to us from the fridge and demanding to be eaten. The aim is to retrain ourselves to slow down, think about what we actually need and only eat when we have made a conscious decision to feed our bodies. The ten stages are tools to help us do just that.

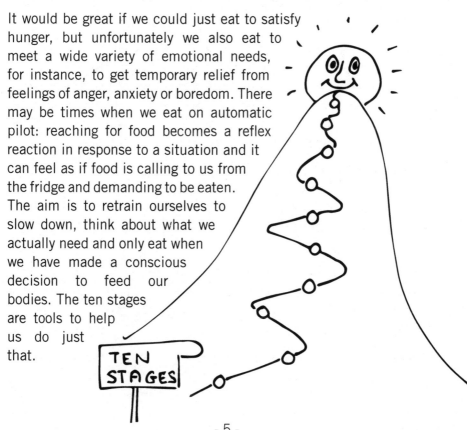

TEN
STAGES

Stage 1: find your motivation: you are more likely to succeed if you know exactly why you want to lose weight and if you are able to collect objective evidence of your progress so you can assess how you are doing at all times.

Stage 2: learn from your past: if you keep doing the same thing, you will get the same results. Your previous attempts at losing weight are a mine of information about all the factors that helped or hindered you last time. Think of yourself as a scientist unpicking what happened before so you can maximise your chances of success.

Stage 3: what needs are you trying to meet? When you overeat, you are probably trying to meet needs other than hunger. If you can learn to recognise what those needs are, you have a chance to intervene to meet them directly and take care of yourself.

Stage 4: write your weight loss plan: to lose weight you need to use more calories than you consume and you are most likely to succeed if you have a clear, specific and achievable plan involving both eating and exercise.

Stage 5: set your goals and build in your rewards: you will be deciding on a realistic goal or set of goals and planning exactly how you will achieve them. This stage is not just about the diet you have chosen, but also how long you will do it, what extra activity you commit to and how you will review your progress. You will also decide on rewards to look forward to which celebrate your achievements.

Stage 6: create your new healthy habits: the key to losing weight and keeping it off is not willpower but creating new habits which complement your goals. Your new habits could be new activities or actions you choose to introduce into your life. Some but not all will be related to food.

Stage 7: manage your cravings: you need to have tactics to deal with the inevitable times when you have an irresistible urge to eat particular foods which are not included in your eating plan (usually comfort food high in carbohydrates or fat).

Stage 8: spot your risk situations: the aim is to know your individual risk situations and to plan in advance how to handle them.

Stage 9: retrain your brain: you will learn to watch out for thinking errors and beliefs around food which may trip you up in your weight loss efforts.

Stage 10: learn from relapse: it is normal to break a diet several times in the process of losing weight. The aim is to expect this, have plans to handle it and not allow yourself to be thrown off course long-term. You will learn to see setbacks as an opportunity to make progress.

This workbook helps you to start from a position of strength: it will help you avoid past pitfalls and design the most supportive plan for you to move forward and achieve your weight goal. It might help to think of it as your own one-to-one counselling session. You will be your own mentor and adapt the tools suggested here to your own situation. This workbook also helps you prepare for what happens after you have successfully lost weight.

The example below illustrates the approach of this workbook.

Example

Sarah has decided to lose weight by having three balanced meals plus three healthy snacks a day. She is upset after a difficult morning. She sits down with a cup of coffee. She eats four chocolate digestives in quick succession.

Sarah has a choice of two possible scenarios:

Sarah panics because she ate food she would normally avoid. She is upset that she has broken her diet. Her brain switches to 'all or nothing' thinking mode: 'I've had four chocolate biscuits I shouldn't have; I might as well finish the packet.' And this is what she does. That evening she has a large pizza and a tub of ice cream while planning to eat nothing and go for a long run the next day.

Sarah is deluding herself that overeating today doesn't count because 'tomorrow is another day' and somehow the clock gets reset at zero. After the first four biscuits, she enters a magical world where normal rules are suspended and she abandons her diet. Look at the alternative scenario where Sarah intervenes immediately rather than giving up her diet for the day:

Sarah stops, slows down her breathing and takes stock calmly. She adds the four chocolate biscuits to her list of foods eaten today and makes a note that she felt tired and hungry after a long and difficult morning. She realises she feels very stressed and decides to slow down and make a list of the jobs she needs to do. She has a hot bath then eats the lunch she had planned. She decides to take her dog for a longer walk than usual in the evening and to call on her friend. She also tells herself to remember to have a healthy snack mid-morning in future. She is happy that she has a plan to keep on track and is very pleased with herself for keeping control of her eating.

Like Sarah, you can learn how to spot the risk situation in advance and to manage it so that you make a deliberate choice instead of eating on automatic pilot.

Think of yourself driving a car: you can only go along the road but you can vary your speed; you can change direction, turn back or stop. The more you know about what lies ahead and the instruments in front of you, the more control you have over your journey.

STARTING A FOOD DIARY

Before you start on your journey, there is one crucial step to take: starting a food diary.

The rationale for this is simple: *what you can monitor, you can control.* Monitoring helps you to change your eating so it becomes a deliberate choice. Keeping a diary can be challenging at the beginning but it will become second nature as you get into the habit. It is worth the effort and you will only need to do it for a while.

Start off by monitoring what you eat for one whole week. Just record everything you eat and drink and where you eat it. It is helpful to make a note of whether you were hungry and, if not, what was going on for you at the time. You don't have to weigh anything but just give an indication of portion size. Please only make a note of what you eat and drink without trying to change your eating. Your records will give you valuable information about patterns and connections between your eating and your mood when you build your plan at Stage Three.

Example

DAY AND TIME	HOW YOU FELT	FOOD OR DRINK	PLACE
Monday 8am	Hungry	1 cup milky coffee 1 bowl cereal 2 slices of toast with butter and jam	Kitchen
11am	A bit bored	1 chocolate bar 1 apple 1 coffee	At desk at work
1pm	Not really hungry but rather tired	1 cheese and ham toasted sandwich 2 bananas 1 small packet crisps 1 cup tea	At desk at work
7pm	Hungry	Battered cod Large portion fries 1 cupful peas 1 bowl ice cream 3 glasses dry white wine	Kitchen
9pm	Bored and restless	1 peanut butter sandwich 3 chocolate biscuits 1 cup of coffee	In front of TV

Exercise 1

Your food diary

DAY AND TIME	HOW YOU FELT	FOOD OR DRINK	PLACE

TIPS

- Don't be tempted to skip this exercise: it is very important because it is your first step in moving from automatic to deliberate eating. It also marks real commitment to yourself to tackle your issues with food.

- Do your best to record what you eat as soon as you have eaten or even before. If you leave it until the end of the day, your record is likely to be wildly inaccurate.

- Recording everything you eat is not something you will have to do forever. Once you understand and address the issues you are dealing with, you will only need to monitor your food consumption occasionally when you have a difficult day.

3

STAGE ONE: FIND YOUR MOTIVATION

WHY DO YOU WANT TO LOSE WEIGHT?

You need to be very clear about why you want to lose weight. There may be several reasons (for example, to improve health, on advice of your GP, to feel more confident on the beach, to prepare for a holiday, for a special occasion, etc.). Writing them down in order of importance will help your motivation.

Example

June has been battling with her weight for the last twenty years. She found out after a routine health check at her GP's that her Body Mass Index (BMI) and her blood pressure were too high. She is breathless when she climbs stairs and she gets very tired running after her small children. She is unhappy wearing loose tops and elasticated waists. She is worried about ending up like her mum who is very overweight and has limited mobility.

Exercise 2

List your reasons for losing weight

-
-
-
-
-
-

ADVANTAGES AND DISADVANTAGES

All change, including necessary change, carries with it some gains and some losses. It is tempting to think only of what you will gain by losing weight. To maintain weight loss, you need to be realistic about the losses as well and to adopt strategies to compensate for them. June has listed below what she thinks her gains and losses might be if she changes her eating habits:

Gains if I change my eating habits	Losses if I change my eating habits
• Lower my blood pressure • Have a healthy BMI • Improve my health and live longer • Buy more fashionable clothes • Enjoy shopping for clothes • Feel more attractive and confident with my partner • Have more energy • Have fewer mood swings • Save money	• I may not be able to eat out as often • I will have to learn new ways of cooking • It might take me longer to prepare meals • Some of my overweight friends may treat me differently • I will miss my chocolate treats • More food will be wasted if I don't finish the children's dinners • I won't be able to drink as much alcohol when I go out at weekends • I will need to find new strategies to cope with negative emotions

June has drawn up a plan to manage possible losses

- Look up new recipes and do more cooking with my family
- Ask some of my friends to be my diet buddies
- Trust my close friends to be happy for me and see me as a good example
- Find some alternative ways of treating myself when I need a 'pick me up'
- Cook smaller portions for my family and include more vegetables
- At weekends have a drink of water in between alcoholic drinks, drink dry wine instead of semi-sweet wine and leave after two hours

Exercise 3

Please complete the exercise below by answering the following questions.

My gains if I change my eating habits	My losses if I change my eating habits
•	•
•	•
•	•
•	•
•	•

My plan to manage possible losses

•

•

•

•

•

COLLECTING EVIDENCE TO CHART YOUR PROGRESS

The obvious piece of evidence is your weight and BMI (look online for NHS healthy weight calculator). There are different opinions about how often it is best to weigh yourself: the PREVAIL Trial found that checking and recording weight daily was more effective but the NHS Eatwell guide and the British Dietetic Association recommend weekly weighing. Choose whatever works for you but don't weigh yourself more than once a day and don't leave it more than a week. Bear in mind that you are looking for sustained weight changes over several weeks and daily fluctuations in weight are normal. Weigh yourself at the same time of day, preferably first thing in the morning with no clothes or shoes.

Example

Carmel printed a weight conversion chart from the internet and highlighted her target range. She records her weight by crossing off lines as she loses weight towards her goal of 11 stones.

Kg	lbs	stones/pounds	
80.3	*177*	*12*	*9*
~~*80.7*~~	~~*178*~~	~~*12*~~	~~*10*~~
~~*81.2*~~	~~*179*~~	~~*12*~~	~~*11*~~

You may like to collect other information which may be better than weight as an indicator of health:

- The size of your waist at its smallest point. The National Institute for Health and Clinical Excellence (NICE) recommends using BMI in conjunction with waist circumference because BMI does not distinguish between body fat and muscle mass nor does it take account of the distribution of fat (NHS Digital, 2020).
- Percentage of body fat (many pharmacies have scales which calculate weight, height, BMI and percentage of body fat and print a ticket for you to keep).
- Blood pressure (taken at your GP's or a pharmacy).
- Personal indicators such as how comfortable you are in your favourite jeans or how long you can jog.
- A series of 'before and after' pictures.

It is sensible to collect more than one measure so you get a full picture.

Exercise 4

List how you will collect your evidence

-
-
-
-
-
-

TIPS

- Beware of a single reason to lose weight which expires at a given time: for instance, losing weight to wear an outfit for a wedding can motivate you up to the wedding but isn't useful afterwards.

- It is worth revisiting your answers on a regular basis: you may discover reasons and gains/losses change over time.

- Don't be tempted to skip this exercise: re-reading your answers will be a great motivator when the going gets tough.

4

STAGE TWO:
LEARN FROM YOUR PAST

If you have spent a lot of time and energy trying diets and putting the weight back on again and more, you may not be keen to examine your history of weight gain and loss. Yet this is rich ground for learning valuable lessons. You have a wealth of evidence which can help you make sense of your past behaviour.

If you keep doing the same thing, you will get the same results. Answer the questions below as truthfully as you can. This time you will go into battle armed with an understanding of the past. You may find it useful to go back and add to this over time.

Remember you are looking at your dieting history rather than just what led you to put weight on in the first place. For instance, someone may think that their original weight gain was linked with difficult emotional issues in childhood: this is relevant but it doesn't directly help them with the 'here and now' of losing weight today. We can't change the past but it is possible to change our behaviour right now. To give an example, a man who was reprimanded as a child if he left any food on his plate may find it difficult to stop eating when he is full. It is useful for him to be aware of this but he can't change his childhood. However, he can do several things in the present to help himself: he could cook smaller portions, put less food on his plate or use smaller plates.

There is an interesting distinction between factors which lead to the start of a problem (precipitating factors) and those which cause the problem to continue (perpetuating factors) (Fairburn, 2013). For instance, a person could put on weight following a sports injury which forces them to be inactive for several weeks (precipitating factor). Working in an office which traditionally has a well-stocked biscuit tin and celebrates all occasions with food treats can sabotage a person's efforts to lose the weight (perpetuating factor).

If you want an in-depth understanding of the reasons for your overeating, it is worth getting hold of 'Understanding Your Eating, how to eat and not worry about it' (Buckroyd, 2011).

To help you reflect on your dieting history, answer the questions below:

Exercise 5

Answer the following questions about your dieting history

- When did you start putting on weight?

- What worked last time you lost weight (A particular diet? An exercise programme? Buddying with a friend?)

- Can you identify particular factors that were linked with you breaking your diet?

- Do you turn to food even though you are not hungry? If yes, when? (Is it when you are sad, tired, angry or bored? To treat yourself? To dampen feelings? To help you sleep?)

- Can you think of specific triggers that usually lead to overeating?

- Do you usually put lost weight back on quickly or gradually?

- **Who, if anyone, supported you or held you back?**

- **What do you need to do differently this time?**

- **What do you need to do the same?**

Can you identify protective factors which kept you motivated last time (disposing of old clothes? going to a gym? having a project? joining a group?)

Example

Selma wrote: 'I was slim as a child and started to worry about my weight at secondary school, particularly in PE lessons when I looked bigger than the other girls. My parents stopped buying biscuits and sweets but I bought and ate them in secret. I put more weight on when I left home and didn't have time to cook for myself. I starved myself into a size 10 for my wedding and have been going up and down, gaining and losing a few stones several times. All the diets I tried have worked for a couple of months at most. I found calorie counting the easiest and I felt fittest when I dieted and went jogging. I think I usually break my diet when I have not eaten enough and feel ravenous or when I am stressed or tired. I have always kept my old clothes because I half expected to put the weight back on again. I tried joining a group and dieting with work colleagues but I felt very uncomfortable sharing personal details.

Exercise 6

What have you learned about your own dieting history?

Imagine telling your story to a very interested loving friend who wants to know in detail exactly what happened:

TIPS

- This is a difficult exercise to do. Most of us would prefer to draw a line over the past and start afresh but it is worth examining what happened to your past dieting efforts. You are looking at the past to repeat only the bits that worked for you. You are working on a strategy to move forward. This will change over time and you may like to revisit it when things don't go according to plan (see Stage 10 on relapse at Chapter 12).

- If you are tempted to skip this exercise, ask yourself why and be honest with yourself. If it is too hard, then tackle the exercise in small chunks.

- Start from a position of strength: identify all the helpful factors which already exist in your life (for some readers it could be playing a sport, having a supportive partner, liking vegetables, preferring savoury to sweet food or enjoying cooking with herbs and spices).

- Treat yourself with kindness. We learn more from positive messages than from criticism. If you tend to beat yourself up, try framing your thoughts differently. For instance, the negative thought of 'I've never kept to a diet in the past for more than three weeks. I'll never manage to lose weight' can be reframed as 'In the past I have struggled with my diets because I tried to lose weight too quickly. I will eat a good balance of foods and reduce sugar in my diet and I will lose weight.' Look in Chapter 11 for more information on dealing with negative thinking.

- If you hear yourself being too critical, ask yourself what a loving friend would say to you in your situation.

5

STAGE THREE: WHAT NEEDS ARE YOU TRYING TO MEET?

When you eat too much you are usually trying to meet needs other than hunger. If you can recognise what those needs might be, you have a chance to intervene and meet them directly.

If you berate yourself every time you think you have eaten too much, remember that what you do is not odd or perverse, it makes total sense. Your brain is wired to seek pleasure and enjoy food. In the short-term, food can be very effective to blot out negative emotions or distract you from what is really troubling you. In the long run, you know that eating more than you need causes all sorts of problems. But you are human and it is normal to choose the immediate reward regardless of the long-term cost.

If you turn to food habitually when you feel stressed, sad, anxious, depressed, bored or angry, you may not even have time to realise what is going on. In the example below, Julia decides to capture the whole sequence of events:

Example

Julia is on her way home after a difficult meeting at work. She spots the supermarket ahead and is very tempted to go in to buy a supersize sandwich and a piece of cheesecake instead of her usual salad and fruit lunch. She decides instead to stop for a minute and analyse the situation objectively:

What has just happened? *I didn't have time to prepare for my meeting. My colleagues asked me some tough questions. I was taken aback and I tried to evade their questions.*

What is going on in my body right now? *I feel shaky and a bit sick. I feel hot because I was stressed and embarrassed in the meeting.*

How am I feeling right now? *I am angry with myself for not being adequately prepared; angry with my boss for keeping quiet instead of supporting me; I am anxious about my future in this job.*

What am I thinking right now? *I made a mess of my presentation. I made a fool of myself. I did a terrible job. I can't face going to work tomorrow.*

What do I really need right now? *In a perfect world I would like total certainty that everything will be OK. I can't predict other people's reactions but I can clarify my options and decide what to do next.*

How can I manage this? *I can review what happened and check how realistic my fears are: when I get home, I will make a list of the questions I was asked and think how I could have answered them. I will consider my options: I could send an email to everyone in the meeting to clarify the information they asked for. I could explain that I don't yet have all the relevant information. I could discuss this with my colleagues tomorrow. I could make a list of the areas I need to learn more about and how I will get that information. I could also wait and see what actually happens tomorrow.*

What do I need to do next? *I will cross the road to avoid the supermarket, go home and change and go for a run to clear my head then have a hot drink before I decide what to do for the rest of the day.*

Are there times when you eat to meet a need other than hunger? Next time use the template below to identify what is happening:

Exercise 7

What has just happened?
What is going on in my body right now?
How am I feeling right now?
What am I thinking right now?
What do I really need right now?
How can I manage this?
What do I need to do next?

Looking back at your dieting history in the last chapter, you may be able to spot frequent occasions when you are tempted to overeat.

Example

Julia has thought about times when she struggled with her eating plan in the past. She has checked her diary for the last two weeks and made a list of the most common reasons for her to overeat when she wasn't actually hungry:

- *To distract herself when she is bored*
- *To put off doing something she doesn't want to do*
- *To blot out her feelings when she is anxious*
- *To increase her energy levels when she is tired*
- *To calm herself when she is angry*
- *To reward herself when she has had a tough day*
- *To join in with her friends when eating out*

She decides to write down beside each occasion what she might do instead of overeating. She checks what is happening and explores more appropriate ways of meeting her needs. She writes down how easy or difficult that was.

What is going on	Alternative to eating	Comments
Boredom	Have an enjoyable book on the go; take a break; change activity	Fairly easy
Putting off a chore	Do the chore for 15 minutes then decide whether to continue or not	Worked well

What is going on	Alternative to eating	Comments
Anxiety	Spend 10 minutes breathing slowly; ask myself 'What is the worst that can happen, what evidence is there that what I am afraid of will happen?'	Difficult to do but will get easier with practice. More effective if I write it down
Tiredness	Take a break for a set amount of time to check whether I am hungry or tired and plan what to do next	Quite challenging. Will help if I have regular snacks
Anger	Make a note of what has happened and list my options	Useful if I do this before I get really cross
Need for a reward	Play an online game, read a book, buy something special, watch a film or listen to my favourite music	I like having something to look forward to
Need to fit in with friends	Plan ahead what I will eat and drink	I will ask my friends to support my dieting

Exercise 8

Can you identify what will work best for you?

What is going on	Alternative to eating	Comments

TIPS

- The exercises in this section are designed to help you take care of yourself. Use them to discover better long-term strategies to meet your needs. Don't be tempted to blame yourself. Talk kindly to yourself and take time to feel proud that you are tackling difficult areas of your life.

- It takes practice to change; start with what is easiest and celebrate your successes.

- There is a useful acronym to check what is going on when you are tempted to eat: HALT - are you Hungry? Angry? Lonely? Tired? You could make up your own acronym to include what is most relevant for you.

- Even if you overeat after doing this exercise, remember that delaying eating by even ten minutes is a major success; congratulate yourself for your courage in facing the truth about your behaviour. The aim of the exercise is to gain understanding, not to limit how much you eat.

6

STAGE FOUR: WRITE YOUR WEIGHT LOSS PLAN

CHOOSE AN EATING PLAN

There are just three steps to follow:

- Make a plan for your eating.
- Record everything you eat and drink and whether you are hungry or eating to meet some other need.
- Decide how you will become more physically active.

We deliberately don't suggest a specific plan because you are unique and will have our own preferred way of losing weight. Do remember that whatever plan you choose, you won't have to follow it forever. You are aiming for deliberate rather than automatic eating. There are many different plans to choose from. The more common methods include:

- Counting calories (don't be tempted to set the limit too low which could be very hard to maintain long-term). Decide on a sensible, achievable number of calories which suits your goals and activity levels. The NHS weight loss plan can help you work out how much weight you need to lose and offers your own personal 'daily calorie intake' based on your BMI to help you lose weight at a safe rate. There is also a World Health Organisation (WHO) healthy eating plan. The British Dietetic Association is also a very good source of information. If you have any underlying health issues with special dietary requirements like diabetes for instance, please check your plan with a health professional.

- Counting 'points' or other units.
- Controlling portion size (for instance, three meals a day with a fistful of protein, hand sized amount of vegetables and palm size amount of carbohydrates like bread, pasta, rice, etc. plus three healthy snacks).
- Following a sensible eating plan, for instance, the NHS Eatwell Guide which gives detailed advice on eating a balanced diet.
- Aiming for three meals and three snacks sitting at the table.
- Selecting two or more of the options suggested in the PREVAIL Trial (Nuffield Dept of Primary Care Health Sciences 2020). This trial evaluated fifty-three distinct weight loss actions under seven headings:

   1. Eating in a structured way (for example 'No calories after 8pm')
   2. Avoiding or swapping specific foods (for example 'Swap unhealthy snacks with six to eight individual nuts')
   3. Changing what you drink (for example 'Drink a pint of water before each meal')
   4. Creating a healthier diet (for example 'Eat only foods with a green nutrition label for total fat')
   5. Meal-time tactics (for example 'Cut food into smaller pieces')
   6. Burning more calories (for example 'Brisk walking for as long as you can')
   7. Be more active as part of your daily life (for example 'Take the stairs whenever you can').

- Setting a time for the next time you eat and planning exactly what you are going to eat (Riley, 2005).
- Restricting what you eat for two days and eating normally for the other five days (5:2 diet plan).
- Practising 'mindful' eating, i.e., being present in the moment and fully engaging with the food you are eating, without distractions and without passing judgement as in the Headspace Diet (Puddicombe, 2012).

If you are unsure about which diet to choose, it is worth reading the NHS Top diets review which gives a useful list of popular diets and their advantages and disadvantages.

Example

Daniel eats healthy food but tends to have very large portions. He decides to count calories because he already knows roughly the calorie content of most foods he eats. He also finds that if he eats more than he planned, it is reassuring to add up the calories straightaway and realise he hasn't consumed that many. That way he can return to his plan quickly.

Obviously to lose weight you need to consume fewer calories than your body needs. If you have tried various diets in the past you will know what works best for you. Your plan should be nutritionally sound (for instance, by following the guidelines in the NHS Eatwell Guide or the British Dietetic Association) and allow you to eat enough so you can keep going long-term without feeling deprived.

DECIDE ON AN EXERCISE PLAN

This need not be any formal exercise; the aim is simply to be slightly more active. If you have not done much exercise recently, start small and build up gradually. It is much easier to keep up exercise which is part of your day-to-day life rather than an add-on. You could decide to get off the bus two stops ahead and walk to your work or you could use stairs instead of a lift. It is very important to make your plan realistic and achievable. For example, if walking to work is a possibility, plan to do it three times a week rather than every day. That way you can still handle rainy days or times when you are in a hurry and you will feel good if you overachieve your goal.

Exercise may not make a huge difference to the number of calories burned unless you take part in endurance sports but any amount will improve fitness and overall wellbeing.

Taking exercise with other people can be invaluable, both from a physical and a social point of view, and it doesn't necessarily need massive commitment: parkruns, for instance, involve turning up in one of many local parks on a Saturday morning and walking, jogging or running up to five kilometres. It is well worth finding out what local initiatives are available locally (like, for instance, Slim2Win, a football initiative for men in Bristol). Simply making a habit of a short weekly walk with one or more friends can be an excellent start.

Start off with activities you know you like, maybe some sport you enjoyed as a child. Or try something new you think you might like. This is a chance to discover some new activity which will be fun and give you added health benefits. There is a wealth of online resources which can be used as a taster.

Exercise 9

Write down below exactly what you plan to do to lose weight and to move more (be as specific as you can):

I will....

Having chosen an eating plan that works for you, you need to commit to recording everything you eat and drink (other than water or black coffee or tea without sugar and all other calorie-free drinks). Monitoring will give you control and will build your confidence. The aim is for you to be aware of what you eat: the easiest way is to write down everything you eat and drink. If you like to measure things, then count calories or portions. You could make yourself a chart and tick items on it. After a while a mental note might do but at the beginning it is best to have a written record of your food consumption. Make your record as soon as possible and preferably before eating because it is very easy to forget if you rely on your memory. Adding exercise taken to your records will help to track your progress and will be a good motivator. You will be able to see how you are improving over the weeks by comparing what you could manage at the beginning with what you can do now. Step trackers can be useful here for you to monitor progress.

BUILDING YOUR CONFIDENCE

An interesting technique to help forward planning is to conduct a 'pre mortem'. Unlike a post mortem which investigates the cause of death, the 'pre mortem' assumes the worst has already happened and works backwards to discover the possible causes, all of this from the safety of the present where all the decisions are still to be made:

Example

Miriam has lost a lot of weight but she is beginning to feel tired of following the same diet and she is dispirited that her weight loss is now getting slower. She doesn't see how she can keep going for much longer. She projects herself forward twelve months:

Worst scenario: I have regained all the weight plus a bit more. My GP is concerned about my risk of getting diabetes and high blood pressure. My clothes don't fit properly and I am back into elasticated pants and big tops.

How did this happen?

I went back to my old eating habits because:

- *I got bored with cooking the same meals of lean meat/fish and steamed vegetables*
- *My social life had reduced to nil because I wasn't meeting my friends for meals or drinks out*
- *I didn't make enough time to cook or take exercise*
- *I didn't keep up with my swimming because it was too much hassle to do it regularly.*

What have I learned from looking into the future? What do I need to do differently now to avoid my worst-case scenario becoming reality?

- *I could try new recipes, vary my meals and plan them in advance*
- *I could organise my shopping and cooking so I batch-cook and freeze interesting meals*
- *I could save some calories every day and have a diet free day at the weekend*
- *I could meet my friends for walks and coffee*
- *I could explore different forms of exercise. I used to love dancing and maybe I could see what is available locally. I cycled a lot as a child and I have often thought of getting myself a bike.*

Exercise 10

Describe your future worst-case scenario

Your worst-case scenario in 12 months' time	
How did it happen?	
What do you need to do now to avoid it happening?	

TIPS

- You need to be able to follow your plan for weeks or months so make it as easy on yourself as possible. Choose a way of monitoring what you eat which is convenient and suits your preferred way of keeping records.

- If you are counting calories, you need to be precise at the beginning. Once you are familiar with the number of calories in the foods you eat regularly, you no longer need to weigh everything you eat but make sure you are fairly consistent: for instance, use the same size cereal bowl every time so you are clear how much you are eating.

- Make sure that you eat enough and that you eat regularly (starving yourself only leads to overeating later).

- Make sure that you eat a good variety of foods: eliminating or restricting one particular group may be unhealthy and sets you up to fail: if bread is your downfall, then have just one or two delicious pieces a day but don't cut it out altogether or you will end up craving it. You could eat lower calorie bread or have no more bread after a time of your choice (say 2pm). Cutting out all fats is also not a good plan because fat makes us feel full and it helps our bodies absorb vitamins A, D and E (see Facts about fat – NHS Eat Well).

- If you drink alcohol, make sure you include this in your diet plan.

- You don't have to keep to the same plan forever. You might find, for instance, that calorie counting works for you to start with but you can just plan your meals for the whole day once you have got used to a new eating pattern.

- Keep it simple: for instance, if you discover that your main problem is eating too much in the evening when you are tired and bored, then make a plan just for the evening.

7

STAGE FIVE:
SET YOUR GOALS
AND REWARDS

Decide on a realistic goal or break it down into a set of goals and plan exactly how you will achieve them. If you have chosen to count calories, decide on the maximum number of calories you will eat every day, how long you will do it for, what extra activity you will commit to and at what point you will review your progress. For instance, you could decide to aim for a set number of calories a day for the next three months to lose up to two pounds a week, to swim once a week and to use stairs rather than lifts at work. You could decide to review progress monthly.

Example

Fiona weights 85kg. She writes in her notebook 'I will be 70kg by my birthday in nine months' time. I will eat 1700 calories during the week and up to 2000 at weekends. I will record the daily number of calories on my phone. I will take a photo of myself every month to see progress and paste it on the fridge. I will give away my clothes as they become too big or get them taken in. I will increase my walking by getting off the bus two stops before the end of my journey. Eventually, I will do the thirty minute walk to work and back four times per week. I will review my progress after my birthday and decide whether I am happy with my new weight or whether I want to lose a bit more.'

Exercise 11

Decide on your goal and how you will review progress

My goal

What I will do to review progress

TIPS

- Be as clear and precise as you possibly can. Be creative and choose the medium that works best for you: use photos, health and fitness apps, step trackers, charts, colours, electronic records, posters on your fridge door, whatever appeals to you – the more vividly you can picture your goal, the better.

- Weigh yourself between one and seven times a week. Remember to look for trends as weight fluctuates naturally on a daily basis.

- If you think you have a lot of weight to lose, it may be worth choosing a series of small goals so you don't get discouraged.

- Be prepared to revise your goals: it might take you a little while and some experimenting before you work out how many calories per day you can sustain without feeling deprived.

- Don't be obsessed by your final goal if it is a long way off; remember the runners' tip: to keep themselves motivated, runners going up a hill look just ahead of their feet and glance only occasionally at the top of the hill they are climbing.

SETTING YOUR (NON-FOOD) REWARDS

As adults, we often feel awkward about rewards. They remind us of childhood and school. We are much better at berating than congratulating ourselves. Committing to a healthy eating plan takes time and is difficult and it is vital to have something to look forward to. The rewards for your weight loss are set by you and they mark a celebration of your achievements. Your brain recognises the positive message 'I am doing well; I have earned my reward and I will keep going.' It is also helpful to be able to visualise something nice to distract you from temptation.

It is particularly important to set rewards if you tend to overeat when your mood is low. It is all too easy on a frustrating day to start having doubts about your progress. If you have set milestones to reach and you have treats to look forward to, you can remind yourself of your achievements and look forward to future successes.

Rewards need not be concrete. You could make a note in your eating plan every time you manage to overcome cravings or you could mentally review your eating at the end of the day and congratulate yourself.

The reward itself is not important but it helps you stay aware of what you are doing in a positive way. Don't be tempted to introduce 'punishments' as well: if you overeat, this is not a reason to beat yourself up. Use the opportunity to learn from the setback as shown in Chapter 12 – Learn from relapse.

Example

Fiona will reward herself with £100 to spend on new clothes for every 3kg lost. She will have a long weekend with her best friend to celebrate achieving her final target.

Exercise 12
Your rewards

TIPS

- Other examples of rewards: an outing, donating money to your favourite charity (a pound for a pound for instance), treating yourself to a luxury item, booking a body massage, buying a season ticket to your favourite football club or museum, adding up the money you used to spend on junk food and takeaways and buying something special with it.

- Exercise trackers which give you a daily/weekly record of steps or activities can be both fun and rewarding.

- Avoid rewarding yourself with food at this point.

8
STAGE SIX: CREATE YOUR NEW HEALTHY HABITS

The key to losing weight and keeping it off is not willpower but the creating of new habits which help you keep to your goal. Of course, some willpower is needed at times but it is impossible to rely on it for every situation in the future.

Think of your overeating as a well-trodden path you have taken in the past in response to tricky situations. Reaching for crisps or biscuits might have become a habit so entrenched that you do it automatically without really thinking about it. Just as a gardener might encourage walkers to take a different route by planting bushes or creating new features, you can create a new response to the triggers which prompt you to overeat. That's where your new habits come in (see the PREVAIL Trial at www.phc.ox.ac.uk for a list of possible actions). Some of these new habits may be new forms of exercise you

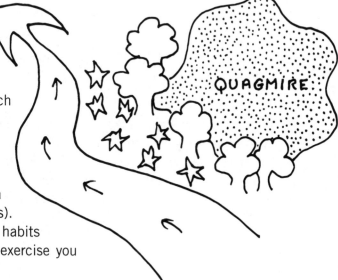

QUAGMIRE

plan to introduce into your life (see Chapter 6). Remember you are the creator of your own landscape and you can redesign the paths if you want to.

Example

Jeremy often eats on automatic pilot and finds he consumes a great deal of food without being aware of it. He decides to aim for three meals a day and three snacks and to create a private ritual to mark the beginning and ending of meals and snacks: he sits at the table, takes five deep breaths and looks at the food in front of him thinking of where it came from, who produced it, etc. After eating Jeremy has a hot drink at the table. He then immediately clears up and throws away any leftovers so he has no opportunity to go back for more.

Create your own ritual: it could be a mantra, a prayer, a form of words which you enjoy, a poem, an image in your head, a set of movements or anything else that works for you. It could be a particular food which marks the end of eating, for instance, eating an apple at the end of every meal.

It is important not to make rules for yourself which are too hard to keep: for instance, 'I will never have seconds' is too extreme. You could commit to a different statement 'I will wait for fifteen minutes before I help myself to seconds.' Other helpful statements might be 'I will eat sitting at the table', 'I will write down what I eat every day.' These rules still require effort on your part but they are more manageable.

If you find it very difficult to resist a particular food, you could set yourself a limit, for instance, 'I will eat a maximum of two doughnuts a week.'

Developing a new habit takes time but eventually temptation will diminish because giving in is just not compatible with what you do. If you almost always choose vegetables or salad instead of chips on a menu, it will eventually become an automatic choice. The aim is to create a new pattern with a new set of habits which minimise the need for you to use willpower.

You are faced with temptation several times a day but the way you define yourself helps you to resist it most of the time: some mornings you may be tempted to stay in bed but, because you consider yourself to be reliable, this is only a fleeting thought which is easily dismissed. Your new habits need to be as automatic as possible, like washing your hands or brushing your teeth. You don't necessarily feel like doing those things but you do them anyway because they are part of your normal everyday routine.

In a sense, you are deliberately redefining aspects of yourself: 'I am a runner and I do five miles a week', 'I play football every Saturday.' You are establishing a new routine which suits the person you are. Don't wait until you feel like exercising; try to make it something you do without thinking, like automatically locking the front door behind you. It helps to imagine how you will feel afterwards. For instance, replace the thought of 'I really am too tired to go for a run this morning' with 'I am going to be so pleased with myself all day when I think of the three miles I ran this morning.'

Remember it takes a great deal of repetitions before a new habit gets established but if you keep at it you will find yourself doing things automatically 'just because that's what you always do'.

Example

Syeda has decided to start small and keep her new habits simple:

- *I will freeze leftovers or throw them away immediately.*
- *I will eat raw nuts instead of salted nuts.*
- *I will eat fruit after a meal and have sweet desserts on special occasions only.*
- *I will not eat in the car.*
- *I will get rid of the biscuit tin at home and talk to my colleagues about doing the same at work.*
- *I will swim once a week and build up to swimming twenty lengths.*

There may be some 'first stages' that Syeda needs to take before she can establish her new habit, for instance, making sure she includes plenty of fruit and vegetables in her weekly shop or buying a swimming costume that fits.

Exercise 13

What new habits will you create? (Think what, where, when, how often and any first stages involved.)

I will

Try and find new activities you can really enjoy: maybe something you always wanted to do but never found the time for or some sport you loved as a child and could start again.

TIPS

- It helps to have good reasons to keep up your new habit: for example, if you meet a friend at the gym or if you are involved in a team sport, you are more likely to turn up so you don't let others down. If you have already booked and paid for a gym class you will have a greater incentive to do it even if you feel tired.

- The less you need to think about doing something that is good for you, the more likely you are to do it. If walking to work is what you do every day, you will easily dismiss the thought of getting in the car or catching a bus.

- Fitness apps which record your steps and your activity can be very helpful. Many of us compensate for a very energetic day by doing a bit less exercise the following day. With a step-counter, for instance, you start again at zero in the morning however busy you were yesterday and it can be very motivating to see how much you have done each week.

9

STAGE SEVEN: MANAGE YOUR CRAVINGS

In this chapter I am not talking about the intense physiological urge to eat when you are very hungry. I am referring to a craving to eat in the absence of hunger in order to meet some emotional need.

I shall use the word 'overeating' to mean either eating excessive amounts or eating food which you would prefer to avoid or a mixture of both. Everyone overeats sometimes whether overweight or not, simply because our brains are wired for survival reasons to find food very tempting. For people who use food to dampen strong emotions, the urge to eat a whole packet of biscuits or a large lump of cheese can sometimes be as intense and overwhelming as true hunger.

This is one of the reasons why we suggested in Chapter 6 that you don't cut out any type of food altogether. If you really like cake and you have a plan which forbids cake, you are bound to feel deprived and be tempted to overeat when you let your guard down. Better to plan for one or two pieces a week that you really enjoy.

WHAT A CRAVING LOOKS LIKE

A craving to eat is a very strong urge to consume particular foods, usually 'comfort' foods high in fat and carbohydrates. It can involve eating something right now or looking forward to eating something later. Sometimes the anticipation of eating is as exciting and soothing as consuming the actual food.

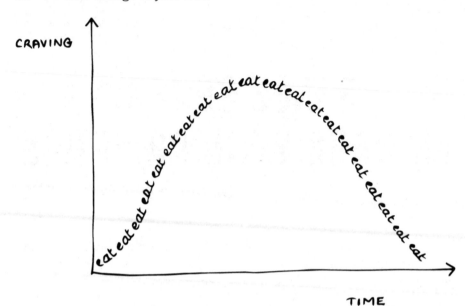

Cravings can be represented as a bell-shaped curve that goes up rapidly, peaks, then subsides. The urge to eat usually grows quickly to a point where it is almost irresistible. At that point, you may feel obsessed with a particular food. The good thing is that cravings don't last even though that may be hard to believe at the time. You can wait until the peak has passed by 'surfing the urge' (observing the urge rise then fall) or by distracting yourself or by delaying eating. The aim is to be fully aware of what is happening instead of reaching for food automatically. This is not about the actual food eaten; it is about retraining your brain to slow down and analyse the situation.

A craving can be likened to a tired toddler who is having a tantrum. Giving in now buys you immediate peace but you are rewarding unwanted behaviour and creating a precedent for the future.

A useful technique involves stepping back and observing the situation objectively. Try rating the craving on a scale of nought (not wanting any food at all) to ten (a desperate urge to eat).

Example

Ravi is tired after lunch and keeps thinking of the snack dispenser in the corridor at work. He rates the craving at nine. He tells himself that he will eat the apple left over from his lunch and make phone calls for the next twenty minutes. Then he will decide whether to buy a snack. Ravi gets absorbed in the task at hand. Half an hour later, he rates the craving at three and decides to wait another half hour. He then realises he is thirsty rather than hungry and makes himself a hot drink. The craving has passed and Ravi is pleased with himself.

You could use a simple rating scale like the one given below to rate and measure your cravings. If you make a note of the time of day as well, you will notice how long it takes for the craving to subside. You may also see a pattern emerging (for instance, a craving for something sweet mid-afternoon could mean you need to eat a more nutritious lunch).

Exercise 14

Measuring your craving

0 = no craving   10 = severe craving

0 ——————————————————————————— 10

TIPS

- Remember that cravings don't last. Anything you do to gain time will help. Try giving yourself permission to eat whatever it is you fancy but doing it tomorrow instead of right now. The craving will have passed long before tomorrow comes.

- It might help to think of a craving as a bad headache: it may be hard to manage in the moment but it is not something you have to deal with forever.

- You might like to build a picture in your mind to see yourself winning over the craving, for instance, you could visualise a big sun melting a pile of snow, a boot crushing an enormous bug, a surfer on a giant wave, a warrior fighting a dragon, etc. Be as creative as you like; having fun will also help distract you.

- If you are able to wait, the craving will dissipate naturally and be replaced by real hunger and you can continue with your plan.

- Remember you committed to monitor everything. If you decide to eat something you had planned to avoid, slow down and record it before you eat. If you can't write it down in advance, record it immediately after. This will ensure you keep control and will help you to minimise the amount you overeat.

COPING WITH CRAVINGS

Willpower alone is not enough. If you eat in response to negative emotions, eating has become your default position. You can reset it by introducing a range of other behaviours which help you change your mood. It is useful to have a list of things you could do when you experience a craving. As you get involved with something else, you break the cycle of automatically giving in to cravings. You also give yourself a chance to change your mind.

Example

Zara is fine when she is busy during the day but she starts to think about snacks after dinner when she is watching TV. She has a list of things to do when she feels tempted:

Going for a walk, jog or cycle

Doing a crossword or a puzzle

Brushing and flossing her teeth

Listening to music

Calling a friend

Exercising for ten minutes

Starting small DIY jobs

Ironing

Cleaning her car

Having a bath

She has promised herself that she will do at least two things on her list before eating. She has started having dinner later and eating plenty of vegetables to fill up. If she does eat after dinner, she sits at the table with the TV off so she does not eat mindlessly. She no longer buys crisps or peanuts but makes sure there is plenty of chewy fruit available like pears and apples. She has also started looking for regular activities she could do in the evening like swimming or a class.

Exercise 15

How will you manage cravings?

Make your plan as specific as possible: for instance, 'If I am tempted to buy a sweet fizzy drink from the shop I pass on my way home, I will either cross the road or buy a newspaper and a bottle of sparkling water.'

If I am tempted to overeat when .... then I will ....

-
-
-
-
-

VISUALISATION

When you experience a craving, you may have a vivid picture in your mind of the food you want to eat. Griffin and Tyrell (2005) describe a very powerful technique: this involves thinking through the worst consequences of the behaviour you want to avoid, visualising them and replacing the picture of what you crave with the picture of the consequences.

Example

Martin tends to overeat when he is anxious. On particularly stressful days he imagines the supersize burger and chips he will get on his way home. The image of the food is overwhelming and he cannot resist the urge to stop at the takeaway and buy his favourite meal. His brain is hijacked by the picture of the burger and the imagined smell of chips and he is unable to think of anything else.

Martin decides to focus instead on the consequences of eating his takeaway meal. He imagines that he is flicking through photos on a screen: he replaces the image of the burger and chips with the image of himself in the evening feeling very disappointed that he has broken his diet after six weeks of working really hard. He sees himself struggling out of bed the next morning because he feels depressed and his confidence is low. Once he has really immersed himself in the 'consequences' picture, he switches to the 'success' picture: he sees himself that evening going for a run with a smile on his face, having avoided the takeaway shop and stuck to his plan. He enjoys visualising how he will spring out of bed the next morning feeling delighted with himself.

Martin's example

My 'craving' picture	My 'consequences' picture
I am cramming a burger and chips in my mouth	I go to bed feeling bitterly disappointed. I wake up in the morning with low self confidence

My 'success' picture
I see myself at home at the end of the day. I have stuck to my plan. I am hugely proud of myself for beating the cravings. I spring out of bed the next morning, delighted with my progress. I see myself stepping on the scales at the weekend having lost another two pounds.

Exercise 16

Next time you feel a strong craving, note the food you crave in the first box. Write the unpleasant consequences of eating that food in the second box. Imagine how good you will feel overcoming the craving and write it in the third box.

Your 'craving' picture	Your 'consequences' picture
Your 'success' picture	

You are not looking for realistic consequences but for whatever would work to put you off eating the food you want to avoid. Martin obviously knows that one large burger and chips are not going to affect his diet in the long-term. The point is that he can switch to the 'consequences' image to stop himself.

If this technique appeals to you, you might like to imagine scenarios involving touch, smell, taste, sound or movement. Adapt the technique to suit you and make it as detailed as you like. If it doesn't work for you, just move on. It is worth mentioning that simply practising observing yourself is very helpful whether or not you manage to resist the craving. You are putting some distance between yourself and the craving and giving yourself the chance to reflect on the situation and make an informed choice. You are also delaying eating which is an achievement in itself.

Quick breathing exercise

To deal with the tension which builds up when you experience a craving, you could try a very simple exercise: sit or stand still and breathe in slowly through your nose. Imagine a cool blue wave travelling from the ground through the soles of your feet and all the way to the top of your head. Then take longer to breathe out through your mouth as the wave washes out all the tension on its way down from your head to your feet and into the ground.

Meditation can also be very useful and there is a wealth of excellent resources online (Headspace diet, NHS Choices Moodzone, for instance).

GENERAL TIPS FOR MANAGING CRAVINGS

- Choose activities which can't easily be done while eating, like painting, shoe cleaning or gardening.

- It is sensible to keep away from areas where food is stored; for instance, tidying a non-food cupboard is better than cleaning a fridge.

- Some of the activities on your list should be small and manageable straightaway.

- It works best if you choose something you enjoy doing or a small chore which you will be pleased to complete.

- You might consider having a place or places where you never eat (for instance, bedroom, bathroom, car) so you have a 'food free zone' to retreat to.

- Try visualising where the craving is in your body then move it to your finger tips and throw it away (or to your toes and kick it away) (McKenna, 2014).

- Athletes visualise themselves winning: can you picture yourself resisting and getting over the craving? Can you see yourself in two hours' time feeling really proud of yourself?

10

STAGE EIGHT: SPOT YOUR RISK SITUATIONS

SPOTTING THE DECISION

Most of us have opportunities to eat at many points during the day and are bombarded by pictures of food everywhere we look. Many of the everyday decisions we take are at least indirectly linked with eating. In a sense, every step we take is either a stage towards or away from overeating. This means that we need to be extra vigilant as we create new healthy eating habits.

What appears as an almost automatic action – eating a sweet – involves a series of steps. The key is to spot the decision to eat before it becomes too difficult to change your mind.

If we analyse the decision to eat a sweet, we can identify several distinct stages:

1. Thinking of eating a sweet
2. Reaching into a cupboard
3. Picking one
4. Unwrapping it
5. Putting it in the mouth.

At stage one you can dismiss the idea of a sweet by distracting yourself. At stage five, with unwrapped sweet hovering over lips, it is still possible to throw it away but it takes a huge effort of will. It is much easier to avoid buying sweets in the first place.

AVOIDING HIGH-RISK SITUATIONS

You can only eat impulsively foods that are available right now: we live in a different environment from ten or twenty years ago and, at least in towns, there are opportunities to snack around every corner. That means more planning is needed. Experiment with making it as difficult as possible to eat foods you want to avoid: you are less likely to eat a packet of crisps if you need to walk fifteen minutes to the corner shop to buy it. It is worth putting up with the inconvenience of buying only small quantities of foods which are very tempting. You could make the foods you want to limit more difficult to consume quickly, for instance, buying nuts in their shells rather than salted nuts. You may also plan ahead how you will cope in any situation where food is somehow 'unlimited', for instance, in a buffet.

Example

Paul knows he can't resist fresh crusty white bread, particularly if spread with salted butter. He has started to buy sliced wholemeal bread and unsalted butter which he finds less appealing. He still occasionally buys his favourite crusty rolls but he only buys one at a time to eat with his meal.

Certain places, times, activities, foods or even people are likely to be associated in your mind with overeating. You may be used to having biscuits with a hot drink in the afternoon. Just looking at your watch will be enough to make you want the food you are used to eating. You can decide to include that food in your diet plan, to substitute a low-calorie alternative or to break the habit altogether. The association will diminish over time until you no longer link a time of day with a specific food. Think of it as a well-worn path which will eventually return to grass if no-one steps on it.

It will be more difficult to cope with situations involving people, as in the example below:

Example

Leo's mum is a wonderful cook who enjoys preparing large quantities of Leo's favourite foods and always insists that he takes food back with him at the end of his weekly visit. Leo has decided to lose weight. Last week he explained that he was counting calories and preferred to have smaller portions. His mum was upset and complained that she had spent a lot of time cooking. Under pressure Leo had second helpings and took the leftovers home.

There is no perfect answer to Leo's dilemma but he has a range of options. He could talk to his mother about his diet before the next visit, explain how important it is and ask for her help. He could eat his mum's meals but refuse to take any food home or he could space out his visits for a while. Some situations are just too risky and avoiding them temporarily may be the only option.

Please remember not to cut out anything altogether. Just plan for what you fancy instead. There is a world of difference between planning to eat a packet of your favourite crisps as part of a meal and impulsively buying the same crisps while paying for petrol. The calories are the same but there is a risk in the second case that you will feel you have lost control.

Example

Jane can't resist peanuts. She has decided that for three months she will cut them out during the week and have a small packet after dinner at the weekend. At the end of three months, she will review her decision.

TIPS

- In time, you will be able to spot danger signals: if you know that you usually want to eat protein when you are truly hungry, then a desire for crisps or biscuits is telling you that you need something but it is not food. It may help to think of a food you like but would not eat for comfort, perhaps a boiled egg. You can then ask yourself 'Would I eat a .... right now?' You could give the test a name of its own to remind yourself (the boiled egg test, the sardine test, whatever your chosen food might be). It would also be helpful to have a good stock of that particular food readily available.

- Plan ahead: make sure you have a strategy to hand if you know your day is likely to be frustrating or stressful. It could mean cooking a healthy meal in advance or planning some activity to keep you busy at the end of the day.

- Try eating only at the table with a knife and fork and eating as slowly as possible so you give yourself the chance to feel full. Concentrate on your food and avoid doing anything else like using your phone or watching TV.

PREDICTING INDIRECT RISKS

Beware of trivial looking decisions which appear to have no connection with food whatsoever yet end up as the first in a string of decisions which lead to overeating.

Example

Tom is driving home after a long day. He is tired and sees a petrol station at the end of the road. He thinks 'I still have half a tank but I might as well fill up to save time tomorrow. I'll get a coffee as well; I need it after the day I've had.' At the checkout, the attendant offers him a large chocolate bar on special offer for just £1. Tom buys two for his children. He then eats one whole bar as he drives home.

There are some key decision points: stopping for petrol unnecessarily, deciding to have a treat, buying two bars of chocolate, unwrapping one and eating it. Tom may have unconsciously decided to break his diet long before he got to the petrol station (for instance, if he ate more than planned for lunch and felt guilty because he has not stuck to plan). Tom has a few alternatives where he would stay in control: realising the potential danger, he could decide to stop for petrol tomorrow, or pay for his petrol on the forecourt, or promise himself an alternative treat in the evening. Tom could decide to include a small bar of his favourite chocolate in his eating plan for tomorrow. He may even realise that chocolate isn't what he wants and choose instead to watch a favourite movie.

Exercise 17

List your risk situations and make notes on how you plan to manage them

Risk situation	How I will manage it
•	
•	
•	

TIPS

- Common risk situations include eating out and family occasions where there are very tempting rich foods and heightened emotions (at Christmas, for example). Most people are likely to lose some control over their diets after drinking alcohol.

- Sometimes the key decision was taken very much earlier in the day. Tom in the example above might have already given himself permission to overeat when he ate a large unplanned packet of crisps with his lunch.

- Remember you always have a choice, including the choice to eat more than you need. The key is to keep monitoring so you stay in control.

- There are times when it is essential to find a way of changing your mood quickly: you could use flip cards, a short sentence, a photo, or imagine yourself in a favourite place. You might consider writing a 'rainy day letter' to yourself telling yourself what your plan is and how much you have achieved already. Schmidt & Treasure (2015) suggest writing two letters five years into the future to a fictional friend: in the first letter you have not managed to lose weight and have been struggling with the consequences. The second letter is happy and upbeat and explains how you lost weight and how your life has improved as a result. Rereading these letters at difficult times can be very powerful.

11

STAGE NINE: RETRAIN YOUR BRAIN

The basis of Cognitive Behavioural Therapy (CBT) is that our thinking, our feelings, our body sensations and our behaviour are closely interconnected. When something happens, it is not the event itself which causes a reaction in us but our perception of it. Our thoughts are particularly important in determining how we interpret the event: imagine that you send a close friend a message to share some exciting news. You expect a prompt enthusiastic reply but your friend doesn't contact you. The way you feel about this and what you do next will depend on what you think is happening. If you think your friend is very busy or their phone is not working, you may be disappointed and leave it a day before sending another message. If you think your friend may be unwell, you will be concerned and you might telephone or visit them. If you think your friend doesn't care about your good news, you will be angry and you may decide not to contact them again for a while. You can see how different interpretations of the same event are associated with widely different feelings and behaviours.

Thinking in unhelpful ways saps our energy and can even be self-fulfilling (See Burns, 1999). For example, a thought like 'I have never managed to stay slim before' is likely to sabotage our dieting efforts. Spotting the exact thought behind the feeling gives us a chance to check the accuracy of the thought: 'I am thinking that I have blown my diet because I ate pizza and chips for lunch. I feel cross and disappointed. However, this is only one meal and I can continue on plan for the rest of the day. I could start making my own healthy pizzas at home so I don't feel deprived in future.' (See the Mind over Mood manual (Greenberger & Paddesky 2016) and also The Feeling Good Handbook (Burns 1999)).

We have a constant stream of thoughts passing through our minds. We can't stop them but we can analyse them and assess objectively how true a particular thought is, and, if necessary, replace it with another more accurate one. Here is an example: Peter has stuck to his diet for four weeks and lost weight steadily. When he steps on the scales at the end of the week, he has not lost any weight. Peter thinks, 'That's awful, I worked so hard for nothing; this diet is not working.' He feels very disappointed. He is tempted to give up on his diet. Peter stops and checks if there is any evidence that his diet is not working: 'I have actually lost 5kg in the last month so this is clearly not true. I do know it's normal for weight to fluctuate.' Peter is still disappointed but he is prepared to keep going and tells himself 'Let's see what the scales say next week. I will plan something nice to celebrate sticking to my diet for four weeks.'

It's important to remember that the relationship between thinking, feelings, body sensations and behaviour doesn't work one way only. The behaviour we adopt in turn has an effect on our thoughts, feelings and body sensations. If Peter gets himself fish and chips for his dinner (behaviour), he will think that he has failed (thought), he will feel overfull and uncomfortable (body sensation) and feel despondent and angry with himself (feelings). If, on the other hand, he carries on with his eating plan, he may soon forget his earlier disappointment when he weighed himself. In other words, we don't have control over events or feelings but we can intervene to challenge our thoughts or deliberately choose behaviours with positive long-term outcomes. Simply waiting a few minutes before taking action, i.e., stopping for long enough to check how we feel, what just went through our mind and what we might do next, is a major achievement regardless of the outcome.

There are several thinking errors which are particularly common for people trying to lose weight:

All or nothing thinking: we see things in black and white. Things are totally good or totally bad with nothing in between: 'If I can't keep to my diet all the time, there's no point in trying.' Try thinking 'grey' instead: 'OK, I ate too much for lunch but that's not the end of the world, I am back on track now.'

'Catastrophising': exaggerating the impact of a minor event and imagining the worst will happen: 'If I eat one biscuit, I won't be able to stop and that's the end of my diet.' Ask yourself instead: 'What evidence do I have that this is true?', 'What is really the worst that can happen?'

Making 'should' statements: telling yourself you 'should', 'ought', 'must' do things sets you up to fail and only makes you feel angry or guilty: 'I should be able to keep to 1500 calories every day', 'He should not buy my favourite cheese when he knows I am dieting.' Try and spot these words and substitute more helpful words: 'I manage to keep to 1700 calories most of the time and I am losing weight'; 'He forgot I get tempted when I see my favourite cheese in the fridge; I will ask him to support me by buying small amounts of low-calorie cheese instead.' Instead of saying 'I must', try saying 'I would prefer'.

Fortune telling: predicting that things will turn out badly even if there is little evidence to support that view: 'I'll never be able to lose weight so there's no point in even trying.' Turn this into a hopeful statement: 'Yes it's hard losing weight but I have done it before and I am ready to do it again.'

Discounting the positive: thinking what has gone well doesn't count: 'I have not lost any weight this week' even though you managed to lose ten pounds in the last four weeks.

Exercise 18

Which error in thinking applies to you most often?

Next time you spot the unhelpful thought, weigh the evidence for and against and replace it with a more balanced thought. Your aim is not to force yourself to think positively but instead to challenge any irrational thinking which hinders your goals.

My negative thought:

What is the evidence in favour of this thought?

What is the evidence against this thought?

My balanced thought:

IDENTIFY YOUR 'RULES' AROUND FOOD

It is not just sudden thoughts which can sabotage our diet efforts; we also need to identify any rules which we have made around food. These are largely unspoken rules which may come from our childhood or our present circumstances but which could impact on our dieting success. Examples of such rules could be: 'I must finish everything on my plate', 'I must never run out of food', 'It's wrong to waste food', 'I should help myself last', 'It's not worth cooking a meal for one person only.'

Examples

Caroline works hard to offer plenty of healthy choices to her three children but she finds it difficult to predict how much they will want to eat on a given day. To make sure she always has enough for them, she holds back and eats small portions with them, then finishes their leftovers. Although she loves fruit, she only eats the least appealing fruit leaving the best for her children. If she fancies something sweet, she eats biscuits because she does not count them as good food for the children.

Roy loves entertaining and always wows his friends with an amazing variety of great dishes. He cooks large amounts because he wants his friends to have a wonderful experience but he ends up with a lot of delicious leftover food which he can't resist.

In both cases, Caroline and Roy's rules can impact on their dieting. Caroline may struggle to commit to a diet if it means buying more food for herself instead of putting herself last. Roy gets left with large quantities of tempting food. Both eat the leftovers standing in the kitchen while clearing the dishes rather than fully savouring food sitting with their family or friends.

It would be very difficult for both Caroline and Roy to change their rules around food; Caroline won't suddenly put herself first and Roy won't lower his standards. However they could experiment to see what actually happens if they make small changes in their behaviour. Caroline could test whether her children would eat less fruit if she doesn't leave the best for them. She could share a bowl of grapes with them and see for herself whether the children notice at all, or are pleased to eat with their mum or maybe even eat more to follow her example. Caroline could reframe her thoughts and make small changes which could help her with her dieting: she could tell herself that her children are her priority and they need a healthy mum so she will invest in her new diet. She could also think in terms of being a good role model when her children see her enjoying a wide range of foods. She might decide to buy more fruit and less of something else.

Roy could try cooking fewer dishes and check whether anyone notices at all and whether his guests are any less appreciative. He could tell himself that his friends won't think any less of him if he produces less lavish offerings. He could try and cook a bit less and draw up a plan to dispose of any leftovers immediately (freezing them, giving them to his guests or neighbours, etc ...).

In both cases, the changes Caroline and Roy may plan are fairly small and may not make a huge difference in terms of calories but they could be crucial in marking a change in their mind-set which asserts their commitment to their diet. More importantly they could mark the beginning of taking better care of themselves generally.

Exercise 19

Can you identify any rules you hold around food which could sabotage your diet?

My rules around food:

How could my rules affect my diet?

How could I test whether this is true or not?

What I could do to help myself?

TIPS

- Once you have identified your unhelpful thought or rule, imagine a good friend tells you that they are thinking or doing something like that. How would you respond?

- If you tend to jump to catastrophic conclusions, try giving a cartoon voice to your thought: imagine Donald Duck or Minnie Mouse saying out loud 'I'll never make it, I am useless!' This might help you see the toxic thought for what it is.

- You could try visualising the toxic thought: for instance, imagine it is a clay pigeon which you shoot in flight. An alternative is to give your thought a label: 'Here comes the end of the world scenario!'

- You could try giving the thought a name, thanking the thought, then dismissing it: 'Thank you "Doom-and-gloom" for worrying about me but I know I can do this.'

- Be aware of the words you use (both when you speak and in your head): 'I will *try* to keep to 1700 calories a day' leaves the door open; 'I *will* keep to 1700 calories five days a week' is decisive – you are doing, not just trying to do. Think and speak positively.

12

STAGE TEN: LEARN FROM RELAPSE

Research has shown that when we work to master a new habit, relapse is a normal part of the process of change. It doesn't matter whether we are trying to eat or drink less, stop smoking or exercise more, at some point we relapse before getting back on track again. Most of us do this several times before we make the change for good. It has been called the cycle of change (Prochaska and DiClemente, 1994). For more information on applying this to food issues, please see The Eating Disorders Association website.

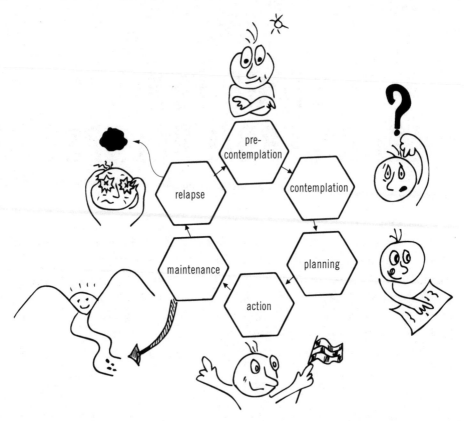

If we apply this diagram to an overweight man at *pre-contemplation* stage, he is not aware of any consequences of being too heavy. *Contemplation* is the stage where he becomes aware of a problem – maybe after his GP recommends losing weight to ease joint pain – and he is beginning to think seriously about it. Once he has decided to lose weight, he works out how to do it at the *planning* stage. He then embarks on a diet and exercise regime at *action* stage. In *maintenance* stage, he has been on a diet for a while and it has become a routine. At *relapse* stage, he breaks the diet. If he can learn from it, he then gets back onto his diet. Or he may be so disillusioned that he gives up altogether (a full relapse) until the need to lose weight becomes evident again and he restarts the cycle.

Another way of looking at it is to think of a slippery stairway. It takes effort to get to the top and sometimes you slip two or three steps and then restart with renewed energy having learned to avoid the treacherous bits. There is a difference between a lapse or a blip (a few steps back – breaking your diet) and a full relapse (falling all the way down the stairs – abandoning the diet).

This has probably happened to you many times in the past and you may sometimes have been so discouraged you stopped dieting altogether. This time be prepared and expect to lapse and don't allow it to throw you off course long-term. It is an opportunity to learn that you can recover your balance and move on.

Example

Julian has managed to lose twenty pounds on his diet. At the end of the week, he jumps on the scales and sees he has put on two pounds. Julian feels depressed and buys himself two pork pies. He continues with a large takeaway and eats biscuits all evening.

Before bed Julian decides to write down exactly what has happened and everything he ate that day. He realises that he hasn't monitored his eating accurately that week and has drunk more alcohol than usual. He remembers panicking at the weight gain and thinking 'This is terrible, I am going to put all my weight back on, I am a failure.' He promises himself to watch out for this kind of thinking next time he is disappointed. He also realises he hasn't spent much time cooking proper meals. He decides to keep better records, to make time to cook every day and to increase his activity levels.

He replays in his mind what he might have done differently: discovering he has put on two pounds, he tells himself 'This is disappointing but not surprising as I have let my guard down in the last few days. Two pounds is not a disaster. I have done very well for the last few months and I will just keep going forward.' He now feels back in control.

This is very different from Dilek's example below where she experiences a full relapse:

Example

Dilek has decided to stop eating sweet snacks for six weeks. She has lost half a stone and is delighted. As she is making a birthday cake, she pops some icing in her mouth. She continues eating all the sweet food she has avoided in the last weeks. It takes a full six months before she is ready to make another attempt at dieting, by which time she has regained all the weight. In hindsight, she can see that cutting out all her favourite foods made her feel deprived. She decides that she will include two biscuits a day and dessert when she eats out in her weight loss plan. She also decides to invite her friend to bake with her next time she makes a birthday cake.

Exercise 20

Can you recall a time you relapsed and what exactly happened?

What was the occasion?

What happened exactly?

How long before you went back to your plan?

DOING A REVIEW

If you 'break' your diet, you might like to try doing a responsibility pie as in the diagram below. This isn't about apportioning blame but it is very helpful to uncover the sequence of events which led to a lapse.

Example

Jane has agreed with her friend to go for a morning jog. She eats a banana and jogs to her friend's. Her friend has overslept and doesn't want to go out. Jane feels disappointed and angry but continues on her own. She loses her way and ends up doing two extra miles. After one hour's jog, she is feeling tired and very hungry. When she gets home, she eats the leftovers in the fridge and a large helping of pasta and cheese until she feels uncomfortably full.

Jane stops and reviews what just happened. She identifies the factors which caused her lapse. She makes a list and puts a percentage by each factor. She also thinks of what she might have done differently.

Factor	How important? Rate it from 0 to 100	What I might do differently next time
Not enough to eat for breakfast	30%	Make time for breakfast and leave later
Disappointed and angry that my friend didn't come	20%	Not in my control but maybe in future we could arrange to call each other first thing
Angry with myself because I got lost, also a bit worried until I found my way again	10%	Carry a phone so I can get directions
Felt very hungry	40%	Pack some nuts in my pocket. Have a healthy meal ready for my return

Jane can easily turn this into the responsibility pie below. This needn't be scientific or complicated. It is just a way of reviewing what happened, making sense of it and learning from it so she is ready next time.

Responsibility pie

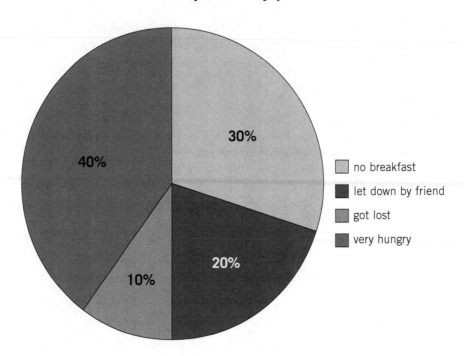

- no breakfast
- let down by friend
- got lost
- very hungry

Exercise 21

Think of an occasion when you had a lapse or a relapse

Factor	How important? Rate it from 0 to 100	What I might do differently next time

Your Responsibility pie

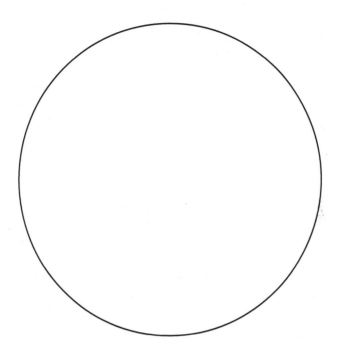

LEARNING FROM SETBACKS

What really matters is not whether you eat something or not but what you learn from your experience. There may be times when you think 'Here I go again; I have broken my diet' but each instance is actually different. According to the Greek philosopher Heraclitus, we cannot cross the same river twice and it can be empowering to figure out what might be different. A good question to ask yourself is 'What is different this time from all the other times this happened?', 'What have I learned?' There may be tiny changes from previous times which will demonstrate how you have actually changed, despite the setback. For example, a person takes a large second helping which was unplanned: this happens regularly but this time they realise that they were tempted because they were very hungry, ate too quickly and the dish was left on the table. This is useful feedback for moving forward.

TIPS

- Do remember to keep recording your food consumption, especially when you overeat. This allows you to keep control and therefore limit the damage.

- Remember that it is during the difficult times that you make the most progress.

- Everyone overeats sometimes and it is not realistic to expect you will be any different. The key is not to let it throw you off course. You are looking for 100% awareness, not 100% compliance with your diet.

- If you gain some weight, catch yourself quickly and get back to your plan. Make a deal with yourself that you will only tolerate putting on a set number of pounds/kilos before you take action.

13

BEYOND WEIGHT LOSS

Whether or not you have already lost any weight, it is crucial to plan ahead anyway. Just imagine how you might feel once you have reached your target weight and try to predict what might happen next.

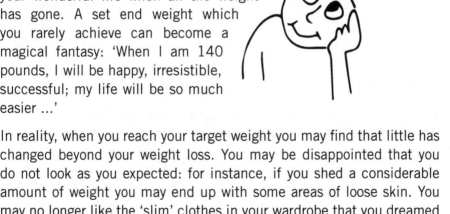

Losing weight is not easy but, for most, maintaining weight loss is even more difficult. You may have kept to a diet for several weeks by dreaming of your wonderful life when all the weight has gone. A set end weight which you rarely achieve can become a magical fantasy: 'When I am 140 pounds, I will be happy, irresistible, successful; my life will be so much easier ...'

In reality, when you reach your target weight you may find that little has changed beyond your weight loss. You may be disappointed that you do not look as you expected: for instance, if you shed a considerable amount of weight you may end up with some areas of loose skin. You may no longer like the 'slim' clothes in your wardrobe that you dreamed of wearing again.

There is a big emotional adjustment to be made as you reach your target. Your life may not be very different and it may be difficult to accept that what you hoped for hasn't quite come true. If you have used food as a way of managing strong emotions, it will take some time to find alternative and better ways of coping. If you feel a little disappointed, it is worth making a list of all the things, big and small, that have improved in your life (a lot of minor changes can add up to a significant improvement in wellbeing).

Example

Joanna lost almost four stones and has maintained her weight loss for a year. She feels fit and can climb stairs without being out of breath. She enjoys shopping for clothes and has a whole new wardrobe. She is much more comfortable with her body but there are still some areas she is unhappy with. She doesn't like the small rolls of fat on her waist and knees which exercise doesn't seem to shift. Mostly she misses her old daydreams of a perfect life at her desired weight. She is healthier and slimmer but nothing else has really changed. She doesn't look like the models in magazines and, although her legs are considerably slimmer, she still struggles to find jeans that look good. Her friends are used to her new size and no longer compliment her on her weight loss.

Yet, unexpectedly, she has discovered a new hobby she loves. She recently completed a five-kilometre fun run for charity with some friends and is very proud of her photo at the finishing line. She got such a sense of achievement that she entered a ten-kilometre race in six months' time.

Exercise 22

What are all the things, big and small, that you think will improve your life on a daily basis as a result of your weight loss?

If you have a lot of weight to lose, the key is to lose it slowly to give yourself the chance to 'fit' into your new body. It is also important to make small changes which will improve your life in the long term. For instance, Joanna started attending classes at her local gym as well as jogging. She enjoys seeing herself get fitter week by week and she has made new friends. She experiments with low fat and low sugar cooking and gets a lot of pleasure from trying new recipes. She says 'no' more often, instead of taking on too much and eating in response to frustration and exhaustion.

In the long term it is small changes that will help you maintain your weight loss. Joanna has found that a few protective factors help her to stay slim, for instance, wearing well-fitting clothes, walking every day, reading more, having something to look forward to and a good friend she can call on if needed.

Exercise 23

What do you think will help you adapt to your weight loss?

TIPS

- You may be tempted to skip this exercise but long-term success depends on planning now so you are ready when you reach your goal.

- It is likely that what makes the most difference to your future wellbeing has little to do with weight (for instance, new habits, activities or friendships).

- You may find that your body naturally remains at a higher weight than what you originally hoped you would achieve. If this is the case, it might be helpful to take a long hard look at how realistic your original goal was.

14

MAINTAINING WEIGHT LOSS FOR GOOD

BEING 'GOOD ENOUGH'

The term 'good enough' was coined by D.W. Winnicott (English paediatrician and psychoanalyst famous for attachment theory) in relation to parenting children. A 'good enough' parent is imperfect but is connected to their child and adapts to meet their needs most of the time. The description of a 'good enough' long-term slimmer is used here to mean someone who has found ways of keeping to a fairly healthy plan and who manages their weight within a range that is acceptable to them. It is also someone who can be reasonably accepting of their shape and body.

Example

Leanne has battled with her weight for years and probably lost several times her body weight, each time ending up a little more overweight. She has been monitoring her eating and has managed to lose two and a half stones. This is less than she hoped but she feels comfortable in herself. For the last six months, she has kept her weight within a range of five pounds, cutting out bread for a few days if she goes over target. She is still worried about her weight and she occasionally overeats. She no longer panics and she knows that she can stay within her range. She walks as much as she can and she enjoys swimming regularly. She is no longer looking for the perfect shape and she is reasonably happy with her image in the mirror.

If you have had a problematic relationship with food for a long time, it is not realistic to expect to be totally comfortable around eating just because you have lost weight. If you can enjoy food most of the time and if you are getting closer to a healthy weight, you have done a remarkable job. Remember to be kind to yourself and pat yourself on the back for your achievement.

At this point it is useful to look back and ask yourself 'What am I doing or feeling differently now compared to the time before I lost weight?', 'What is it that I must continue doing?' Each of us is unique and your solution to overeating applies to you only.

Example

Martha has achieved a healthy weight which is sensible for her. She is less preoccupied with her size and her eating. When she is tempted to eat even though she is not physically hungry, she asks herself 'What is my body telling me right now? Am I tired, thirsty, bored, sad or angry? What do I really need?' She no longer fights her body by punishing it with restrictive diets, over-exercising or squeezing it into tight clothes. Most of the time she does not count calories but she has a rough idea of how much she has eaten every day. On stressful days when she is in danger of overeating, she returns to careful monitoring of her food and moods.

She recognises the key factors which reinforce her new good eating habits: being aware of what she eats, not skipping meals, eating slowly, enjoying a balanced range of foods, snacking on fruit and nuts, having a to-do list to manage cravings, doing new physical activities which she loves and having a collection of clothes in her wardrobe which she enjoys putting on in the morning. She is still apprehensive when she steps on the scales at the end of the week but she is confident that she can manage to keep within her target range.

In this example, you will notice that there is no single magical ingredient to Martha's success but a new approach which keeps her on target. Her excess weight has gone but the urge to overeat has not disappeared altogether. The difference is that she can manage it better and now feels confident she will remain in control.

SUPPORT FROM A HELPER OR A GROUP

Is losing weight something intensely private for you or do you think it would be good to have support from a helper or a group? You may change your mind about this as you go. If you want support from others please see below what to look for.

An individual helper: the ideal person is someone you feel comfortable sharing personal information with and whom you trust to keep your issues to his/herself. It should be someone who is not emotionally involved, i.e., someone who wants the best for you but who is otherwise neutral about your weight (a partner who really wants you to lose weight is obviously not suitable). Make sure your helper has no current weight issues of their own (a friend who wants to lose weight could introduce an element of competition). Your helper needs to be a good listener; remember that you are the expert at dealing with your own issues. You don't need to be told what to do, but someone who is interested and asks questions will help you discover more for yourself. Most of all, your helper needs to be kind, loving and honest, but never critical.

A group: it may be very helpful to get together with others to work your way through this workbook. Make sure you are clear from the beginning how your group will run:

• How long is it to run? (It is best to set a limited number of sessions at the start and review as you go.)

• Is membership open (anyone can join at any time) or closed (only people who start at the beginning can belong)?

• Set ground rules at the beginning: confidentiality (What information can be shared outside the group? For instance, you could agree that members can share information with outsiders about themselves – something they learned about themselves in the group – but nothing about another member). Agreeing commitment to the group is important (for instance, turning up on time and sending apologies if unable to attend). It is important to agree in advance that members will listen to each other without interruption and that only supportive comments will be made. It is worth agreeing who will manage the group (members could take it in turn to facilitate the meeting).

- One helpful question to think about beforehand is 'How will you know the group is working for you?'

Please remember that a group can help you slim even if it is unrelated to food. For instance, joining a group that you enjoy (a football team, a gym class, a choir, a book club, a dance or painting class, a walking group or your local parkrun) may give you huge support because it gives you pleasure, friendship and a chance to feel good about yourself.

15

INFORMATION FOR FAMILY, FRIENDS, CARERS AND PROFESSIONALS

You may be a family member, a partner or a friend worried about a loved one's excess weight or you may be responsible for someone's care in a professional capacity. Please take from this chapter whatever suggestions are relevant to the role you are fulfilling.

The aim of this workbook is to adapt to weight loss common techniques derived from Cognitive Behavioural Therapy (CBT). CBT is generally used to help people with depression, anxiety and addiction problems. This does not mean that the person you are supporting is suffering from a mental health problem, it is simply that this approach is very useful to help people change and, in this case, to keep to whatever diet they have chosen to follow. The aim of the techniques we recommend is to help the slimmer become aware of their thoughts, feelings and potential triggers so they can eat in a healthy way rather than overeating on automatic pilot. It allows them to become their own coach, able to identify how their thoughts and feelings are affecting their behaviour around food. They can then control their eating most of the time and plan ahead to avoid potential pitfalls. It is a process of learning and experimenting in a very practical way to find out the best way for them to control their eating. The workbook doesn't specify any particular eating schedule as any sensible plan will work if it is followed through. The exercises in this workbook are designed to train the mind to adopt healthier eating and lifestyle habits.

Losing weight successfully takes time and is difficult and keeping it off even more so. Understanding and monitoring one's own behaviours around food is a major challenge. It takes courage for your loved one to work through this workbook and they deserve encouragement and compassion for their efforts.

Some of the techniques in this workbook will appeal more than others. If something doesn't quite work, it can be tried again at a later stage or adapted to fit. It can be immensely helpful for slimmers to share what they have learned about themselves with a kind person.

WHAT IS YOUR ROLE?

There is a wide range of roles for concerned others from the very basic (doing your best to avoid putting temptation in their way) to full involvement (actively witnessing their learning and exploration). Whatever it is, and it may change over time, your job is to be a benign supporter of their efforts, not to make sure they stick to their diet. They are in the driving seat at all times. The aim of the techniques described in this workbook is to increase awareness; the weight loss itself is the result of that new learning rather than the primary goal.

The first thing is to clarify exactly what your role is:

Exercise 24

What is your relationship to the person trying to lose weight? (partner, relative, friend, carer, professional?)

....

In what relevant areas are you involved with that person (for instance, cooking for the slimmer, eating with them, shopping, spending leisure time, exercising, working, supporting them in a professional capacity)?

....

Are you personally affected by his/her weight issue? (It is crucial to recognise at the onset how you might be affected: for instance, if the slimmer is your partner and has put on a lot of weight, you might wish they looked like they did when you were first attracted to them and you are then directly involved.)

....

What exactly is your job here?

....

Have they asked you to help with weight loss? (It's easier for you if you have been asked directly but, if not, that's fine too: you can still be supportive indirectly.)

....

If you have been asked to help directly, are you happy to do this? (Beware of taking responsibility for their weight loss: you are the cheerleader, not the controller.)

....

WHAT YOU CAN DO

The greatest gift we can offer another human being is to actively listen to them, without interruption and without deflecting the conversation to another topic that springs in our own mind. Very often there is no need to say anything: giving the other person a chance to voice their thoughts aloud may be enough to help them make sense of their experience.

Some would-be slimmers are very secretive about their weight problem and may not want to share anything. This may be difficult to accept but that is fine too, there is still a huge amount you can do to support them. In some ways the most helpful thing is what you don't do: for instance, if you share a home with your loved one, it goes without saying that buying, cooking or eating foods they have decided to cut out or limit in their diet will put temptation in their way. There may be a difficult balance to strike here.

Example

Gemma is supporting her partner Mei in following a low carbohydrate diet. They have two small children. Gemma and Mei have agreed to cook larger portions of vegetables and to plate up meals rather than leave dishes on the table. Mei's plate has smaller carbs portions but is loaded with extra vegetables. Left-overs are either frozen or thrown away immediately. Mei can't resist chocolate so they have agreed to only buy a very small supply of her least favourite brand and to keep it out of sight.

All the actions above are small but they are very supportive to Mei.

There are many helpful things which you can do which have nothing to do with food: for instance, making it possible for your loved one to join in exercise activities or to attend slimming groups. Providing childcare, taking over some household chores or welcoming changes in normal routines (like an early start on Saturday mornings to attend a local parkrun) can be invaluable.

WHAT IS BEST AVOIDED

Remember you are at the edge of a lake helping someone to get out. You can shout encouragement, throw a buoy or a rope but don't wade in and get wet yourself.

Don't save your loved one from uncomfortable feelings. When they complain they haven't lost as much weight as they hoped, saying 'You look lovely as you are' or 'It's not your fault, you have a slow metabolism' is meant kindly but it isn't helpful. Acknowledge their feelings and go for facts: 'You're disappointed but I've seen you run up the stairs comfortably.' Or ask instead: 'What do you think happened?', or 'What are you planning to do next?', or 'What can I do to support you?' Try to focus on the learning rather than the weight itself.

Example

Zoe suggested to Tania a particular diet which really worked for her. Tania is following it and has already lost 2 kgs. Every time they meet, Zoe checks on Tania, asks her how much she weighs and how she is doing on the diet. Tania is getting resentful and puts off seeing Zoe when she knows she hasn't lost as much as she hoped.

In this example Zoe has done her job sharing a useful diet and is now too involved. She should wait for Tania to talk about her diet if and when she chooses.

Don't tell your loved one what to do: it will only make them rebellious. Remain positive and reinforce all the good things they do to control their eating and ignore everything else.

Don't overinvest: it's not a fight but even if it were, it isn't yours. However supportive you are, they are the ones who decide what they put in their mouths. If you put considerable effort into helping your loved one with their diet (for instance, preparing elaborate calorie-controlled meals), you will only become frustrated when they break the diet. Keep things normal.

EXPECT SETBACKS

It is very difficult to lose weight and it is normal to go off the rails several times during the process, particularly when someone has a lot of weight to lose. This approach is about learning a new way of dealing with food and we all know from experience that it takes time and a few mishaps before we can master a new skill. The main thing is for the slimmer to learn from the setback and get back on track as soon as possible (see Chapter 11 about dealing with negative thoughts and Chapter 12 on relapse).

Setbacks are unavoidable because this is the normal pattern when changing a behaviour. It takes many repetitions before a new habit is acquired for good. If you are going to support your loved one over a long period of time, it is very important that you are kind to yourself and look after your own needs. The change in your loved one's eating habits, however welcome, may also be disruptive of your own routine and it is normal to experience frustration at times.

WHAT HEALTH PROFESSIONALS CAN DO

If you are working with the slimmer in a professional capacity, you already have experience and your own way of addressing weight issues with your clients or patients. You also have two crucial advantages over a 'lay' helper: first of all, you are in a unique position to motivate the slimmer. While a relative will be seen as nagging, you have the authority and the legitimacy to comment on the importance of losing weight. It is part of your role to point out the current and future consequences of excess weight. In the bewildering wealth of slimming diets, you can recommend a sensible plan which you can then easily discuss at future appointments. You probably know of any services or groups which are available for slimmers in your local area. You may also be able to offer desirable 'rewards', for instance, a reduction in blood pressure medication.

Secondly you are able to provide objective feedback (see Chapter 3) in a way no one else can. For instance, you could suggest the slimmer uses one of the machines in GP surgeries and pharmacies which measure weight, BMI and blood pressure and produce a printout for discussion at the next appointment. If you see someone regularly, you are able to provide a set of milestones they can attach goals to, for instance, 'I will be 2 kg lighter by the time I have my next medical appointment.'

There is a large evidence base for the effectiveness of brief interventions for weight management in primary care. Beyond the obvious questions about weight or dieting, taking an interest in the slimmer's new habits can be extremely supportive.

TIPS

- You don't have to guess how to support, just ask 'How can I best help you with this?' The answer may well change over time and you may need to renegotiate your degree of involvement.

- If you have never had weight issues and struggle to identify with the slimmer, try using your own experience of a behaviour you may have tried to change in the past (for instance, relating to smoking, drinking, exercising, watching TV...).

- Beware of offering rewards if you are a friend or relative: by all means suggest nice things to look forward to but don't make them conditional on weight loss or on any particular behaviour.

- Be mindful of what may be risky times for your slimmer: for instance, eating out with friends, going out to a buffet or having a takeaway.

- If you can, share in any physical activity. It is more fun to walk, jog, swim with a companion.

- If you are seriously worried about a loved one's weight gain or loss, talk to a GP or call one of the organisations listed in the Appendix.

16

CONCLUSION

This workbook is all about you regaining control of your eating by monitoring both your food consumption and your thoughts and feelings. I hope that you have been able to act as your own weight loss coach, making sense of what happened when you tried to lose weight before. I have offered a range of strategies for you to monitor your eating, handle cravings and manage risk situations, spot unhelpful thinking and learn from setbacks. Crucially I have encouraged you to look beyond achieving your target and see how to deal with the reality of your new slimmer self so you can maintain your weight loss.

What you are doing is difficult and the vast number of weight loss books is proof that there isn't a failsafe way of doing it. I don't offer a quick fix but instead a gradual increase in your awareness of your relationship with food. Think of yourself as a captain steering a tanker: it takes planning and effort to change direction but inch by inch you build momentum and keep going until you are on track. You are not simply losing weight; you are changing your eating habits for good. Be proud of yourself for getting this far and remember that you alone hold the key to your success. It really is a case of the journey being more important than the destination: you tend to focus on the target weight but the learning takes place as you make your way there – during the gradual weight loss. It is during the journey that you develop the new coping skills and learn the new habits which will prove life changing in the long run.

Example

A year ago, Adam was seriously overweight. His weight is now at the top end of the healthy range for his height. He is thrilled with his progress, not just his new shape but the increase in his confidence. He goes out more, has become a great cook and has started playing squash. He still occasionally craves takeaways and sweet fatty snacks when he is bored or tired but most of the time he eats when he is hungry. He no longer eats automatically in response to negative emotions. He is content with the way he looks and his new way of life. He understands his own issues around weight and he has the tools to keep the weight off long-term.

Adam imagined that being slim would be life changing. Actually, he really enjoys small pleasures like wearing the colours he likes rather than dark slimming colours, the comfort of loose waistbands, running for buses and his GP no longer commenting on his weight or blood pressure. If he overeats, he understands what is going on and can regain control quickly. In the past, it might have taken him several months to get back on track but now it is a matter of hours or days at the most.

REVIEWING YOUR PROGRESS

Exercise 25

Think back on your progress so far and list below at least three ideas or techniques that you take away with you for the future:

1.
2.
3.

Exercise 26

Rate your confidence

On a scale of 0 to 10, how confident do you feel that you can lose the weight you still want to lose or maintain your weight loss?

.... out of 10

What would it take for you to increase that rating by half a point? (For instance, if you answered 5 out of 10, what would need to happen before you could answer 5 ½ or even 6 out of 10?

....

....

....

....

....

....

A FINAL MESSAGE

If you have managed to start using this workbook to lose weight, you should be extremely proud of yourself. If you haven't yet reached your goal, take heart, you may need to adapt this approach so it works better for you. Either way, trust your amazing body to know what is good for you and to do its very best. Remember most progress is made during the difficult times because you gain strength from facing your issues and coping.

Carla, a wonderful Tai Chi teacher, tells her students 'Don't worry about knowing every movement, go with the flow, enjoy yourself and be splendid!'

17

USEFUL RESOURCES

Your GP: if you are seriously concerned about your weight or your health, s/he should always be your first port of call.

Start the NHS weight loss plan – NHS. Also available as an app on the App Store and Google Play.

Look at the website of the British Dietetic Association (BDA) at bda.uk.com

Parkruns: for information about 5k events in local parks see www.parkrun.org.uk

If you think you may be suffering from an eating disorder, look up Beat, the UK's eating disorder Charity at www.beateatingdisorders.org.uk

To find an accredited counsellor, contact the British Association for Counselling and Psychotherapy (BACP) at www.bacp.co.uk

If you have suicidal thoughts, please contact The Samaritans (www.samaritans.org)

18

REFERENCES AND BIBLIOGRAPHY

Branch, R. and Willson, R., (2012), '*Cognitive Behavioural Therapy Workbook for Dummies*', Second edition, John Wiley & Sons, Inc.

Buckroyd, J., (2011), '*Understanding Your Eating, how to eat and not worry about it*', Open University Press, McGraw Hill, Glasgow.

Burns, D.D., (1999), '*The Feeling Good Handbook*', Penguin Books.

Cooper, P., (2009), '*Overcoming Bulimia Nervosa and Binge-Eating, A self-help guide using Cognitive Behavioural Techniques*', Robinson, London.

Department of Health and Social Care, (27 July 2020), 'Tackling obesity: government strategy', at www.gov.uk

Fairburn, Dr C., (2013), '*Overcoming Binge Eating, The Proven Program to Learn Why You Binge and How You Can Stop*', The Guilford Press, New York and London.

Greenberger, D. and Padesky, C.A., (2016), '*Mind over Mood*', The Guilford Press, New York.

Griffin, J. and Tyrell, I., (2005), '*Freedom from addiction, the secret behind successful addiction busting*', HG Publishing.

Harris, R., (2008), '*The Happiness Trap, Based on ACT: a revolutionary mindfulness-based programme for overcoming stress, anxiety and depression*', Constable & Robinson, London.

McCartney, Dr J., (2014), '*Stop Overeating, the 28 day plan to end emotional eating*', Vermillion, London.

McKenna, P., (2014), '*Freedom from Emotional Eating*', Bantam Press.

NHS Digital, Publication, Part of Statistics on Obesity, Physical Activity and Diet, England, 5 May 2020 at digital.nhs.uk

NHS, Eatwell – NHS, www.nhs.uk, Eatwell Guide.

NHS, Top diets review at www.nhs.uk

NHS 12 Week Weight loss plan – Better Health at www.nhs.uk/better_health

Nuffield Department of Primary Care Health Sciences, (2020) PREVAIL Trial, University weight loss study, 'Overview of 53 Weight Loss Actions', University of Oxford, see www.phc.ox.ac.uk

Prochaska, J., Norcross, J. and DiClemente, C., (1994), 'Changing for Good, a program for overcoming bad habits and moving your life positively forward', Harper Collins.

Puddicombe, A., (2012), 'The Headspace Diet', Hodder & Stoughton Ltd.

Riley, G., (2005), 'Eating Less – Say Goodbye to Overeating', Vermillion, London.

Sattyn, E., 'Secrets of Feeding a Healthy Family, How To Eat, How To Raise Good Eaters, How To Cook', Kelcy Press, 2008.

Schmidt, U., Treasure, J. and Alexander, J., (2015), 'Getting Better Bit(e) by Bit(e), A Survival Kit for Sufferers of Bulimia Nervosa and Binge Eating Disorders', Institute of Psychiatry London UK, Routledge, London and New York.

Shirran, M. and M., (2013), 'The Gastric Mind Band, the Proven, Pain-Free Alternative to Weight-Loss Surgery', Hay House UK Ltd.

ACKNOWLEDGEMENTS

I owe a huge thank you to my family, Dee, David and Lyra for their constant help and encouragement.

Also to Alice Solomons, Publishing Director of Free Association Books who made the workbook happen and showed endless patience to me, as someone new to publishing.

And to Dr Sanju George, my friend and mentor who held my hand throughout.

And to all the dear friends who supported me: Carole Hodson, Calvin Richards, Lynn and Peter Burke, Dr Jane Quinn, Denise Riley, Jo Englisch, Nawal El Jarroudi, Tania Cagnoni, Mark Saxon, Jacqui Clements and Leah Wells.